This is a Robert Frederick
This edition published in 2005
© Robert Frederick Ltd, 4 North Parade, Bath BA1 1LF, UK

Printed in India

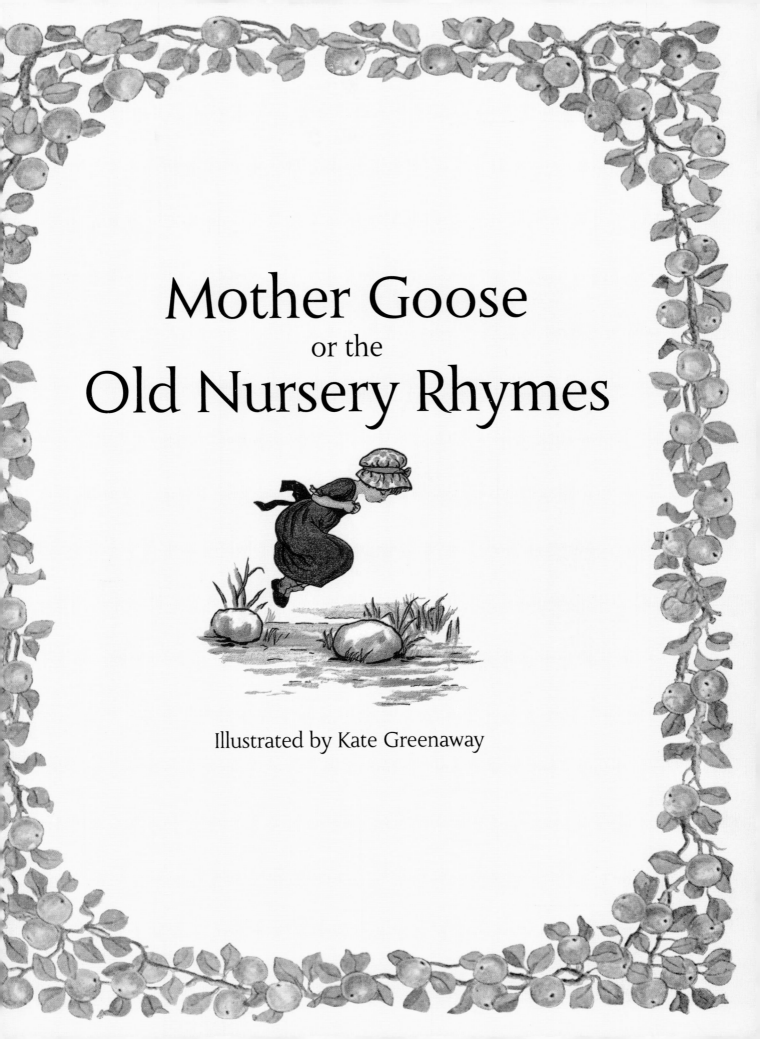

Mother Goose
or the
Old Nursery Rhymes

Illustrated by Kate Greenaway

ark! hark! the dogs bark,
The beggars are coming to town;
Some in rags and some in tags,
And some in silken gowns.
Some gave them white bread,
And some gave them brown,
And some gave them a good horse-whip,
And sent them out of the town.

Johnny shall have a new bonnet,
And Johnny shall go to the fair;
And Johnny shall have a blue ribbon,
To tie up his bonny brown hair.

There was a little boy and a little girl
    Lived in an alley;
Says the little boy to the little girl,
    "Shall I, oh, shall I?"
Says the little girl to the little boy,
    "What shall we do?"
Says the little boy to the little girl,
    "I will kiss you!"

Jack and Jill
Went up the hill,
To fetch a pail of water;
Jack fell down
And broke his crown,
And Jill came tumbling after.

Daffy-down-dilly
has come up to town,
In a yellow petticoat
and a green gown.

Lucy Locket, lost her pocket,
Kitty Fisher found it;
There was not a penny in it,
But a ribbon round it.

L ittle Tommy Tittlemouse,
Lived in a little house;
He caught fishes
In other men's ditches.

Tell Tale Tit,
Your tongue shall be slit;
And all the dogs in the town
Shall have a little bit.

illy boy blue, come blow me your horn,
The sheep's in the meadow,
the cow's in the corn;
Is that the way you mind your sheep,
Under the haycock fast asleep!

Girls and boys come out to play,
The moon it shines as bright as day;
Leave your supper, and leave your sleep,
And come to your playmates in the street;
Come with a whoop, come with a call,
Come with a good will, or come not at all;
Up the ladder and down the wall,
A halfpenny loaf will serve us all.

A dillar, a dollar,
A ten o'clock scholar;
What makes you come so soon?
You used to come at ten o'clock,
But now you come at noon!

L ittle Betty Blue,
Lost her holiday shoe.
What will poor Betty do?
Why, give her another,
To match the other,
And then she will walk in two.

Mary, Mary, quite contrary,
How does your garden grow?
With silver bells, and cockle shells,
And cowslips all of a row.

Rock-a-bye baby,
Thy cradle is green;
Father's a nobleman,
Mother's a queen.
And Betty's a lady,
And wears a gold ring;
And Johnny's a drummer,
And drums for the king.

Here am I, little jumping Joan,
When nobody's with me,
I'm always alone.

Goosey, goosey, gander,
    Where shall I wander?
Up stairs, down stairs,
And in my lady's chamber;
There I met an old man,
Who would not say his prayers;
Take him by the left leg,
Throw him down the stairs.

Little Tom Tucker,
He sang for his supper.
What did he sing for?
Why, white bread and butter.
How can I cut it without a knife?
How can I marry without a wife?

Little Miss Muffet,
Sat on a tuffet,
Eating some curds and whey;
There came a great spider,
And sat down beside her,
And frightened Miss Muffet away.

Elsie Marley has grown so fine,
She won't get up to serve the swine;
But lies in bed till eight or nine.
And surely she does take her time.

We're all jolly boys,
and we're coming with a noise,
Our stockings shall be made
Of the finest silk,
And our tails shall trail the ground.

See-Saw-Jack in the hedge,
Which is the way to
London Bridge?

L ittle lad, little lad,
Where wast thou born?
Far off in Lancashire,
Under a thorn;
Where they sup sour milk
From a ram's horn.

My mother, and your mother,
Went over the way;
Said my mother, to your mother,
"It's chop-a-nose day."

Georgie Peorgie, pudding and pie,
Kissed the girls and made them cry;
When the boys come out to play,
Georgie Peorgie runs away.

As Tommy Snooks, and Bessie Brooks
Were walking out one Sunday;
Says Tommy Snooks to Bessie Brooks,
"To-morrow—will be Monday."

Ring-a-ring-a-roses,
A pocket full of posies;
Hush! hush! hush! hush!
We're all tumbled down.

One foot up, the other foot down,
That's the way to London town.

Book of Tunes

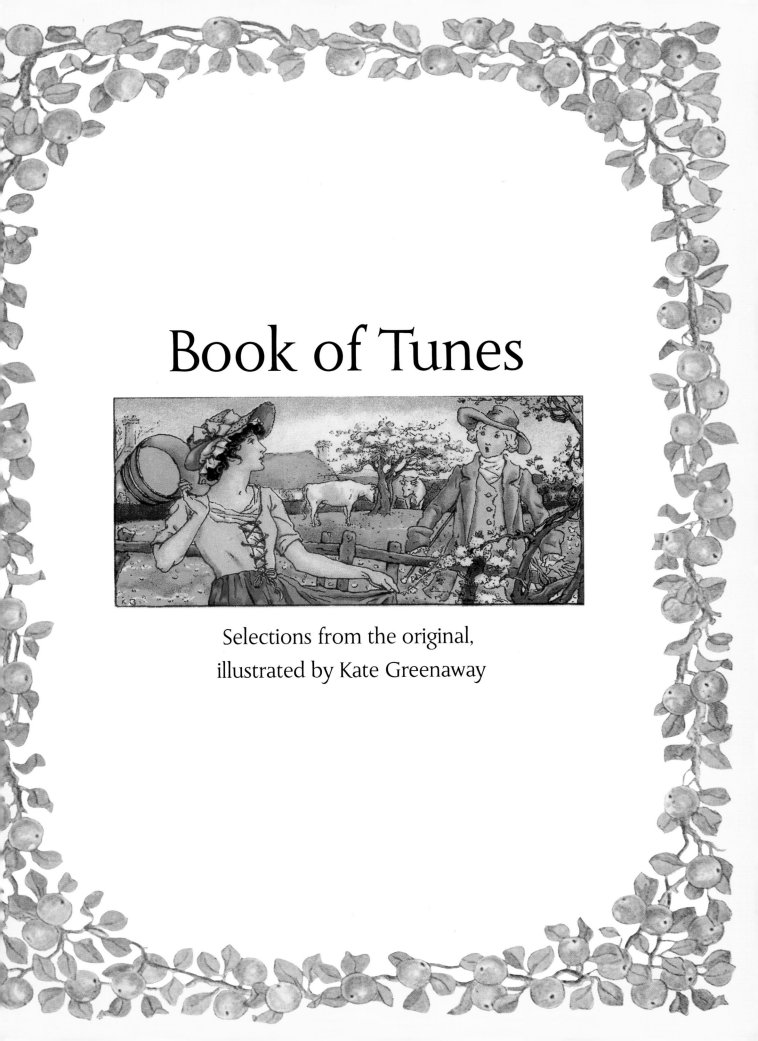

Selections from the original,
illustrated by Kate Greenaway

WHERE ARE YOU GOING TO, MY PRETTY MAID?

Where are you going to, my prett-y maid? I'm go-ing a-milk-ing, Sir, she said. May I go with you, my prett-y maid? You're

kind-ly wel-come, Sir, she said. Who is your fath-er, my prett-y maid? My fath-er's a far-mer, Sir, she said. Say will you

ma-rry me, my prett-y maid? Yes, if you please, kind Sir, she said. What is your for-tune, my prett-y maid? My

GENTLE JESUS, MEEK AND MILD

Slow.

Gen - tle Je - sus, meek and mild, Look u - pon a lit - tle child; Pit - y my sim -
Fain I would to Thee be brought, Dear-est Lord, for - bid it not; In the king - dom

Ped.   Ped.   Ped.   Ped.

JACK AND JILL WENT UP THE HILL

Jack and Jill went up the hill to fetch a pail of wa-ter, Jack fell
down and broke his crown, and Jill . . came tumb-ling af - ter.

slowly . . . .

quicker . . . .

Ped.

SING A SONG OF SIXPENCE

Sing a Song of Six-pence, a pock-et full of rye . . Four and twen-ty black-birds baked in a pie . .

When the pie was o-pen'd the birds be-gan to sing . . Was not that a dain-ty dish to set be-fore a King.

Curly Locks, Curly Locks, wilt thou be mine ?
Thou shalt not wash dishes nor yet feed the swine,
But sit on a cushion and sew a fine seam,
And feed upon strawberries, sugar, and cream.

H ush-a-bye, baby, on the tree top,
  When the wind blows the cradle will rock;
  When the bough breaks the cradle will fall,
  And down comes baby and cradle and all.

Jack and Jill went up the hill
To fetch a pail of water;
Jack fell down and broke his crown,
And Jill came tumbling after.

Little Miss Muffet
Sat on a tuffet,
Eating her curds and whey;
When down came a spider,
And sat down beside her,
And frighten'd Miss Muffet away.

Mary, Mary, quite contrary,
How does your garden grow ?
With silver bells and cockle shells,
And pretty maids all of a row.

Little Polly Flinders
Sat on the cinders,
Warming her little toes;
Her mother came and caught her,
And scolded her little daughter,
For spoiling her nice new clothes.

Sing a song of sixpence, a pocket full of rye,
Four-and-twenty blackbirds baked in a pie;
When the pie was open'd the birds began to sing,
Was not that a dainty dish to set before a King.

Pussy Cat, Pussy Cat, where have you been ?
I've been to London to look at the Queen.
Pussy Cat, Pussy Cat, what did you there ?
I frighten'd a little mouse under the chair.

Where are you going to, my pretty maid ?
I'm going a-milking, Sir, she said.
May I go with you, my pretty maid ?
You're kindly welcome, Sir, she said.
Who is your father, my pretty maid ?
My father's a farmer, Sir, she said.
Say will you marry me, my pretty maid ?
Yes, if you please, kind Sir, she said.
What is your fortune, my pretty maid ?
My face is my fortune, kind Sir, she said.
Then I won't marry you, my pretty maid
Nobody ask'd you, Sir, she said.

Gentle Jesus, meek and mild,
Look upon a little child;
Pity my simplicity,
Suffer me to come to Thee,
Gentle Jesus, meek and mild.

Fain I would to Thee be brought,
Dearest Lord, forbid it not;
In the kingdom of Thy grace
Grant a little child a place,
Gentle Jesus, meek and mild.